My Little Book of
Farm Animals

by Daphne Hogstrom
illustrated by Carl and Mary Hauge

A Golden Book · New York
Western Publishing Company, Inc.
Racine, Wisconsin 53404

Do you suppose
When a cow says MOO
That she's really asking,
"How do you do?"

Do you suppose
When a horse says NEIGH
That he means "I'm hungry.
May I have some hay?"

And do you think
When a chickadee SINGS
That he really means
"What fun to have wings!"

Do you suppose
When a chipmunk SQUEAKS
That he's really saying,
"See my chubby cheeks!"

?

Do you suppose
That a goat's gruff BLEAT
Means "I like tulips
And daisies to eat!" **?**

And do you think
When a goose HONKS clear
That she's really calling,
"Just look who's here!" **?**

Do you suppose
When a piglet SQUEALS
That she's really saying,
"How *fine* mud feels!"

?

Do you suppose
That a puppy's BARK
Means "Let's hurry home
Before it's dark!"

And do you think
That a cat's MEOW
Means "A dish of milk
Would taste good now!"?

Do you suppose
When bees BUZZ by
That they're really asking,
"Would you like to fly?"

Do you suppose
That a mouse's EEEEEEK!
Means "I nearly was caught
By Cat last week!" **?**

And do you think
That a donkey's BRAY
Means "Come on. Let's go
On a trip today!" ?

Do you suppose
That a duck's loud QUACK
Means "I'm taking a shower,
So please step back!" ?

Do you suppose
That a rooster's CROW
Means "Wake up, sleepyhead.
Get dressed and go!"?

And do you think
When a lamb BAAAAs low
That he's really saying,
"Someday I'll grow!"

Do you suppose
When they squeak or squawk
That animals
Really, truly talk?

They don't talk to me
Or my sister or brother,
But I *know* they talk
To one another!